Ralph Vaughan Williams

MASS IN G MINOR

For S.A.T.B. soli
and double chorus

FABER ***ff*** MUSIC

NOTE

This Mass is, of course, intended to be sung unaccompanied; the 'organ introductions' are only to be used in case of necessity to give the pitch at the start and to restore it if lost during the course of a movement.

Organists are particularly asked *not* to modulate from the key to which the chorus may have fallen, during the course of the movement, back to the true key.

An *ad libitum* organ part has been added, which may be used if it is not found practicable to sing the Mass entirely *a capella*.

R.V.W.

Copyright 1922 by Ralph Vaughan Williams
First published in 1922 by J Curwen & Sons Ltd
This edition copyright © 1990 by Joan Ursula Penton Vaughan Williams
The edition first published in 1990 by Faber Music Ltd
3 Queen Square London WC1N 3AU
All rights for the United Kingdom, Eire, Canada,
Australia, New Zealand, Israel, Jamaica and South Africa
administered by Faber Music Ltd
Printed in England by Caligraving Ltd

ISBN 0-571-51192-9

Duration: c. 25 minutes

To buy Faber Music publications or to find out about the full range of titles available please contact your local music retailer or Faber Music sales enquiries:

Faber Music Limited, Burnt Mill, Elizabeth Way, Harlow, CM20 2HX England
Tel: +44 (0)1279 82 89 82   Fax: +44 (0)1279 82 89 83
sales@fabermusic.com   www.fabermusic.com

To Gustav Holst and his Whitsuntide Singers

MASS IN G MINOR

FOR S.A.T.B. SOLI AND DOUBLE CHORUS

RALPH VAUGHAN WILLIAMS
(1872-1958)

I. Kyrie.

4

5

CURWEN

CURWEN

2. Gloria in excelsis.

✤ INTONATION. (TENOR VOICE.)

Glo - ri-a in ex-cel-sis De - o.

✤ Or the intonation proper to the day.

✱ To be used only when the chorus have lost pitch in the previous movement.

CURWEN

CURWEN

CURWEN

CURWEN

CURWEN

3. Credo.

※ To be used only when the chorus have lost pitch in the previous movement.

CURWEN

CURWEN

CURWEN

CURWEN

CURWEN

CURWEN

4. Sanctus–Osanna I–Benedictus–Osanna II.

✻ To be used only when the chorus have lost pitch in the previous movement.

CURWEN

CURWEN

CURWEN

Osanna I.

Benedictus.

(senza Ped.)

CURWEN

CURWEN

Osanna II.

Moderato maestoso.

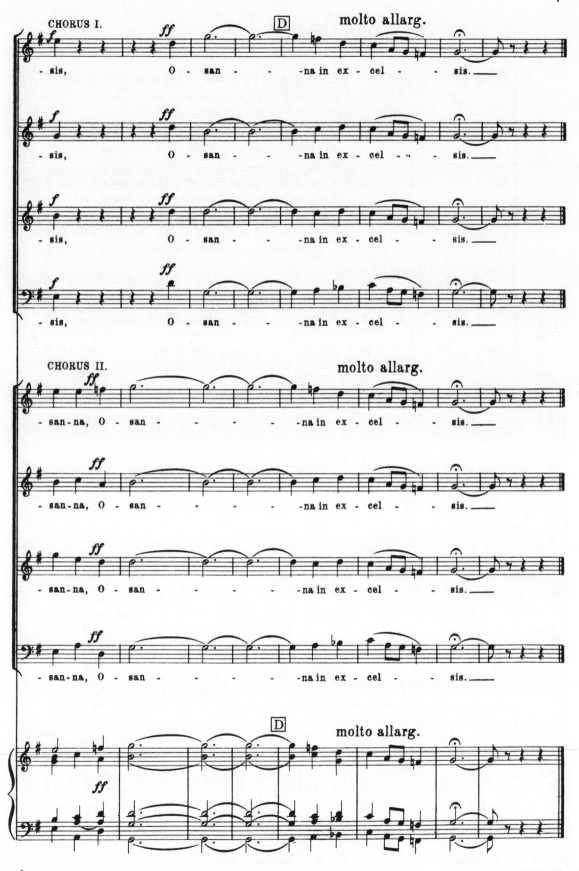

5. Agnus Dei.

✱ To be used only when the chorus have lost pitch in the previous movement.

43

3642

CURWEN

CURWEN

Choral Programme Series

Consultant Editor: Simon Halsey

The Faber Music
Choral Programme Series

This highly acclaimed repertoire series is now a well-established programming tool for many choirs. The series, spanning both mixed- and upper-voice repertoire, offers a wealth of fresh material from the fifteenth century onwards.

With editions of the utmost integrity and practicality—keyboard reductions, singing translations and informative introductions are all included—the series aims to assist choirs, large and small, in concert programming.

Representing unprecedented value for money, each volume is a minimum of thirty-two pages and contains up to forty minutes of music.

Selected volumes for mixed voices

FABER *ff* MUSIC

Faber New Choral Works

General Editor: Simon Halsey

Faber New Choral Works introduces a wealth of new or recently written
choral music to choirs in search of fresh repertoire.
The series draws in a rich diversity of living composers and includes both lighter
and more challenging contemporary works, offering a thrilling array of varied styles.

Faber New Choral Works

Faber Music Ltd. Burnt Mill, Elizabeth Way, Harlow CM20 2HX
Tel: +44 (0)1279 82 89 82   Fax: +44 (0)1279 82 89 83
sales@fabermusic.com   www.fabermusic.com

FABER **ff** MUSIC